Helicopters and Gingerbread

THEODORE CLYMER: SENIOR AUTHOR

GINN AND COMPANY
A XEROX EDUCATION COMPANY

CONTRIBUTING AUTHORS
DORIS GATES
ELEANOR G. ROBISON
ELIZABETH F. RUSSELL

CONSULTANTS
ROGER W. SHUY: LINGUISTICS
E. PAUL TORRANCE: CREATIVITY

ARTISTS · ROBERT AMUNDSEN, HILLARY HAYTON

0–663–25156–7

CONTENTS

AT THE ZOO

4

5

Who Said "Hello"?

Bill said, "Come with me, Ben.
I want to see the zoo."

Ben said, "Stop, Bill!
Who said 'hello'?
Who said 'hello' to me?"

"We will see," said Bill.

BIRDS

Ben said, "Help me, Mother.
Who said 'hello'?
Who said 'hello' to me?"

Mother said, "Can't you guess?
Guess who said 'hello,' Ben."

"I can guess," said Jill.

" A parrot ! " said Bill.

" This parrot can say ' hello. ' "

" Hello, " said the parrot.

" Hello ! Hello ! "

Ben said, " You can say ' hello ' !

Say ' hello, ' Parrot.

Say ' hello ' to me. "

9

The Seal

Ted said, " Hello, Bill.
Do you want to see the seal ? "

" Yes, I do, " said Bill.
" Come, Ben.
We will see what a seal can do. "

10

Ben said, "No!
I like this parrot.
It can say 'hello.'"

"The seal can swim," said Ted.
"And it can play ball."

"Seals can't play ball!" said Ben.

"This seal can," said Ted.
"Come and see it, Ben."

"Here is the seal," said Bill.
"It can play ball, Ben."

"It can! It can!" said Ben.
"Come here, Dad.
This seal can play ball."

Dad said, "Yes, it can, Ben.
The seal likes to play
with the ball."

"I like the seal," said Ben.
"It can swim and play ball.
But it can't say 'hello.'

I want you to see the parrot, Dad.
I want the parrot to say 'hello'
to you."

Little Elephant

Nan said, " Come here, Jill.
Come and see this elephant. "

"What a little elephant!"
said Jill.

Kay said, "Help me, Dad.
I can't see the elephant."

Dad said, "Here you are, Kay.
Can you see the elephant?"

"I can! I can!" said Kay.
"The elephant wants to swim."

18

"It can't swim here,"
said Dad.

"But it can play.
Elephants play like this, Kay."

Kay said, "Here comes a man.
Who is he, Dad?
Is he the zoo man?"

"Yes, he is," said Dad.

"The elephant sees the man,"
said Kay.
"This elephant can run, Dad."

20

" Here, little elephant, "
said the man.
" You will like this. "

Kay said, " I can guess
what the elephant wants.
Can you guess, Dad ? "

The Little Goats

"I want to see the goats,"
said Bill.

"Here they are, Ted."

Ted said, "We can play
with the goats.

Here they come, Bill."

22

23

Bill said, "Look at this goat.
He wants something, Ted."

"Hello, little goat," said Ted.
"Do you want something?

Do you want to play with me?
What do you want?"

"The goats don't want to play," said Jill.

"They want something to eat."

Nan said, "Help the goats, Ted. This is what they want you to do."

Ben said, "I want to help this goat.
I can get something for it to eat."

"I will help you," said Dad.
"Here you are, Ben."

"Stop, Goat!" said Ben.
"I can get this for you.
Can't I help you?"

Jill said, "See me swim.

Look at me swim fast."

Bill said, "See what I can do.

Look at me hop in."

it	is	in	ill
fit	his	pin	will

This page provides for the recognition and reinforcement of the vowel correspondence /i/ *i* as in *fit* through the decoding of new words and the review of known words.

27

hid	bit	Tim	kit
hide	bite	time	kite

Tim said, "Do we have time for a ride?"

Dad said, "Yes, but don't you want a kite?"

Tim said, "No, I don't.

I want a ride.

I can get a ride for a dime."

This page provides for development of the "set for diversity" in decoding new words with the correspondences /i/i as in <u>kit</u> and /ay/i__e as in <u>kite</u>.

Signs for the Zoo

This man has some signs
for the zoo.

Do you know where he will put

the signs ?

This page provides for vocabulary expansion through the
introduction of new words in a meaningful context.

29

HELICOPTERS

WHAT CAN HELICOPTERS DO?

A man wants help.

He sees a helicopter.

He wants to get in it.

Who is in the helicopter?

What will he do?

This man can't swim.

He wants help.

The man sees a helicopter.

Who is in the helicopter ?

What will he do ?

This man wants a ride.
He wants a ride
to the airport.

Here comes a helicopter.
It will stop for the man.
He will ride to the airport
in the helicopter.

34

The animals want something.
What do they want?

Here comes a helicopter.
A man is in it.
He comes with something
for the animals.
It is something the animals
will eat.

Here comes a helicopter.

It comes with something big.

It comes with something

this man wants.

The helicopter is little.

But it is a big help.

What can the helicopter do?

Will it stop here?

A man said, "Who will go
for a ride with me?
Who will go for a ride
in this helicopter?
Get in! Get in!"

Who wants a helicopter ride?
Will the helicopter go fast?

39

The Surprise

Dad said, "Here we are, boys.
This is the airport."

Bill said, "Is the surprise here?
Is it something we can do?"

Dad said, "The surprise is here.
It is something boys like to do."

40

41

"What a big airport!" said Ted.
"Look at the helicopters, Bill."

"A helicopter ride!" said Bill.
"Is the surprise a ride
in a helicopter?
Did we guess, Dad?"

"Yes, you did," said Dad.
"And here is the helicopter.
Get in, boys."

The man said, "Here we go.
Did you guess the surprise?"

"Yes, we did," said Ted.
"This ride is a big surprise."

Dad said, "Boys like surprises.
And I like to ride in a helicopter."

"Look, boys," said the man.
"Can you see the zoo?"

"I can," said Bill.
"But I can't see the animals.
I guess they are too little."

"Look for the elephants,"
said the man.
"They are not too little."

"I can see a big elephant
and the goats," said Ted.
"But I can't see the parrot.
It is too little for me to see."

"I like this ride," said Bill.
"This is the ride for me!"

A Funny Ride

Here is a funny old helicopter.
A parrot is in it.
The parrot likes to ride
in the funny old helicopter.

46

The parrot said, " Hello, Bill.
Do you want to ride with me ? "

" Yes, I do, " said Bill.
" This is a funny old helicopter,
but I will ride in it. "

" Hop in, " said the parrot.
" Hop in, Bill. "

"I can see the zoo," said Bill.

"Look here, Parrot.

Are you the zoo parrot?

Did you say 'hello' to Ben?"

"Yes, I did," said the parrot.

"I said 'hello' to Ben.

He likes me."

Bill said, " Can I make
the helicopter go ? "

" Yes, you can, " said the parrot.
" Make the helicopter go. "

Bill said, " I like a fast ride.
Will this old helicopter
go fast ? "

" Yes, it will, " said the parrot.
" You can make it go fast. "

Bill said, " Here we go
for a fast ride."

"Stop! Stop!" said the parrot.
"This is not funny.
Stop the helicopter."

"I can't!" said Bill.
"I can't make it stop.
Help me, Parrot.
Help me!"

53

Dad said, "I will help you.
What do you want, Bill?"

"I want you," said Bill.
"I don't want the parrot.
He is not funny.
I don't like the old helicopter.
And I don't want to ride in it.
Don't go, Dad.
I want you here."

EXERCISES

This page provides for recognition of the correspondence /e/<u>e</u> as in <u>hen</u> through the decoding of new words, and for the review of known words. 55

red   men   set   led   met

read   mean   seat   lead   meat

Who will lead the boys
to the park?

56

bed	pet	bill	miss
bell	pen	bib	mill

a duck with a bib

a pet with a bell

a goat in a pen

This page provides for recognition of the correspondences /e/<u>e</u> as in <u>bed</u> and /i/<u>i</u> as in <u>bib</u> through the decoding of new words.

A BOOK FOR KAY

Read To Me

Dad said, "Here is a lion.
And here is a little mouse."

Kay said, "What will the lion do
to the mouse?
Read the book, Dad.
You read, and I will look
at the animals."

THE LION AND THE MOUSE

Lion said, " Hello, Mouse.

I want something to eat.

I will eat you. "

" Don't eat me, " said Mouse.

" Let me go, Lion.

Let me go.

And I will do something for you. "

Lion said, "You can't help me.
You are too little."

"Yes, I am little," said Mouse.
"But I am not too little to help you.
Let me go, and you will see."

63

Lion said, " I will let you go.
Run fast, Mouse. "

" I will surprise you, "
said Mouse.
" You will see what I can do. "

Lion said, "Help! Help!
I want to get away from here,
but I can't."

Mouse said, "Here I am, Lion.
I will help you get away from here."

Lion said, "You can't help me.
You are too little."

Mouse said, " No, Lion.

I am not too little to help you.

I can help you get away from here. "

"Do something fast,"
said Lion.

"A man will come and get me.
He will get you, too."

Mouse said, "Look here, Lion.
See what I can do."

Lion said, "You did help me!
You are little, Mouse.
But you did something big for me."

"Yes, I did," said Mouse.
"But you did not eat me, Lion.
You did something for me, too."

The Gingerbread Boy

Little Old Woman said,
" Look here, Little Old Man.
We want a little boy.
I can make a gingerbread boy
for you and me. "

And Little Old Woman did.

Little Old Man said,

" Come here, Gingerbread Boy.

I want to see you. "

" No ! " said Gingerbread Boy.

" I will not come to you.

I will run away from you. "

And Gingerbread Boy did.

Big Dog said, "Stop! Stop!
I want to see you.
Come here, Gingerbread Boy."

Gingerbread Boy said, "No!
You want to eat me, Big Dog.
I ran away from Little Old Man
and Little Old Woman.
I will run away from you, too."

And Gingerbread Boy did.

Little Goat said, "Stop! Stop!
I want to see you.
Come here, Gingerbread Boy."

Gingerbread Boy said, " No !
You want to eat me, Little Goat.
I ran away from Little Old Man
and Little Old Woman.
I ran away from Big Dog.
I will run away from you, too. "

And Gingerbread Boy did.

Fox said, "Stop! Stop!
You can't swim, but I can.
I will swim, and let you ride.
Come here, Gingerbread Boy.
Let me help you."

And Gingerbread Boy did.

Fox said, "Here we are,
Gingerbread Boy.

You ran from Little Old Man
and Little Old Woman.

You ran from Big Dog
and Little Goat, too.

But you can't run away from me !
I will eat you. "

And Fox did.

Big toys.   Funny toys.

Little toys.   Animal toys.

What toy would you choose?

Tim wants a bell for his bike.

Bess wants a funny seal.

Jim wants a toy to ride.

This page provides for review of the correspondences /i/i as in Jim and /ay/i__e as in bike, as well as reinforcement of the correspondences /e/e as in bell and /iy/ea as in seal.

EXERCISES

This page provides practice in locating objects whose names contain the sound /iy/ as represented by the letters <u>ea</u> in <u>eat</u>, and <u>ee</u> in <u>bee</u>.

EXERCISES

bed	seal	feet
bet	seat	feed
bell	seam	feel

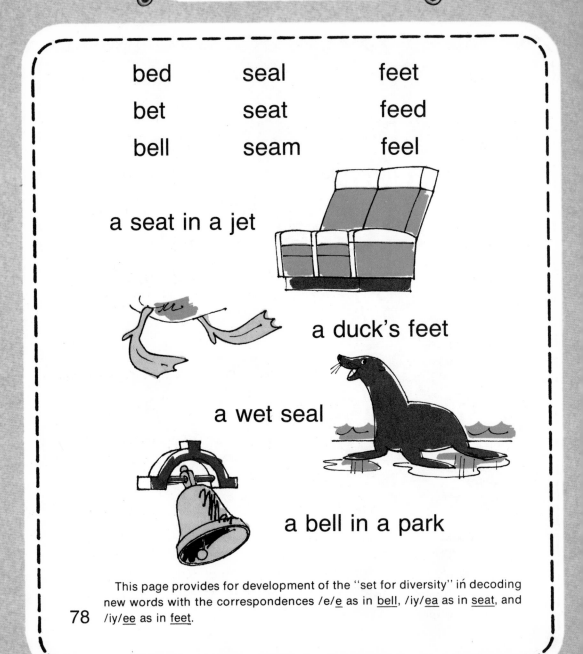

a seat in a jet

a duck's feet

a wet seal

a bell in a park

This page provides for development of the "set for diversity" in decoding new words with the correspondences /e/<u>e</u> as in <u>bell</u>, /iy/<u>ea</u> as in <u>seat</u>, and /iy/<u>ee</u> as in <u>feet</u>.

78

• New Words in This Book •

Unit I

4. zoo
6. who
   hello
9. parrot
   say
10. seal
12. play
    ball
13. Dad
16. elephant
17. Kay
20. man
    he
22. goats
    they

24. something
26. for

Unit II

31. helicopters
32. in
34. airport
35. animals
36. big
38. go
40. surprise
    boys
42. did
44. too
46. funny

old
49. make

Unit III

59. lion
    mouse
62. let
63. am
65. away
    from
69. gingerbread
    woman
71. dog
    ran
74. fox

To the Teacher: *Helicopters and Gingerbread,* Level Four, Reading 360, introduces 38 new basic words and maintains the 58 words presented in *My Sound and Word Book* and *A Duck Is a Duck.* Plural and possessive forms of words are not listed separately. Words printed in color can be decoded independently.

• Words for Decoding Practice •

The following words, grouped by similar elements, have been presented in this book.

e	ee	e_e	ead	eal	eat	et	ed	en	es
he me we	see	here	read	seal	eat	get let	Ted	Ben	yes

The following words, also grouped by similar elements, may be decoded independently by the pupils, utilizing the skills learned in *Helicopters and Gingerbread*. Words shown in color were presented on exercise pages of this book. These groupings of words may be used to develop additional decoding lessons. See T. E. for uses.

be	bead	beak	beam	beep		bed	bet	bib	Bill	bit
bee	beef		bean	beat		beg		big		
				beet		bell				
				deep	dear		den	dig	dim	
					deer		hen			
	feed	feel		feet	fear	fed		fib	fill	fit
						fell		fig		
		heel		heap	hear			hid	hill	his
				heat						hit
				jeep			jet			
				keep				kid	Jill	
									Jim	
								kid	kill	kiss
										kit
	lead		lean	leap		led	less	lid	lip	
	leaf					leg	men			
		meal	mean	meat			mess		mill	miss
							met			
				neat	near		net			
Pete		peek		peep			pen	pig	pill	pit
		peel					pep		pin	
						Ned	pet			
		real			rear	red		rib	rip	
	seed		seem	seat		sell	set		sip	sit
tea			team		tear	tell	ten		till	
									Tim	
									tin	
wee	weed	weak				well	wet	wig	will	
		week							win	
							yet			

PRINTED IN THE U.S.A.